Dílis go hÉag

Tiomnaítear an t-amhránleabhar seo do chuimhne Bhriain Uí Uiginn — Brian na Banban — múinteoir, scríbhneoir, file, staraí agus saighdiúir i gcúis na hÉireann. Rugadh é i gCill Scíre, Co. na Mí ar 1ú Iúil 1882.

Bhí Brian Ó hUiginn gníomhach i gConradh na Gaeilge i dtús an chéid seo agus throid sé in Ard-Oifig an Phoist le linn Seachtain Ghlórmhar na Cásca 1916. Bhí sé ina Theachta Dála d'Iarthar an Chláir ins an gCéad Dáil.

One task which Brian Ó hUiginn performed with enthusiasm and distinction was that of perpetuating the memory of the men and women of 1798. For years he published the Wolfe Tone Annual in which he fearlessly told the truth of Ireland's long struggle for freedom. He returned again and again to the '98 period. He was a prolific writer of songs and verses in both Irish and English and right up until his death in 1963 he had an optimistic outlook and an unfailing faith in the capacity of Irish youth to continue the struggle.

"Freedom's bright and blessed day!
Ireland free from Saxon sway!
Lift your hearts and pray God speed ı
To the dawning of the day!"

GW00671394

The day will dawn again also for the writi

In presenting once more, some of the Songs of 1798 to the Irish public, it is appropriate that we should also remember some of Brian Ó hUiginn's close associates, friends who survived the youthful martyrs and were blest with long lives. Cathal Ó Murchadha (1880-1958) fought in Bolands Mills in 1916 and was also a Teachta Dáil Éireann and Sinn Féin member of Dublin Corporation; Seosamh Ó Cléirigh (1881-1976) fought at Mount Street Bridge and published much of Brian's work; Séamus Funge (1891-1973) was the printer who ensured that the Irish people could always read the Republican message. His father-in-law Patrick V. Mahon, had been printer to An Claidheamh Soluis. Like the great O'Donovan Rossa, each one of them was an "unconquered and unconquerable man", unassuming and dedicated to the cause of Ireland.

Bhí siad uilig dílis go héag.

Seán Ó Brádaigh,
Eagarthóir.

1

Diary of an Expedition
Humbert's Army of Ireland, 1798

July 19:
The French Directory authorises the sending of three expeditions to Ireland and gives command of the first one to General Humbert.

August 6:
General Humbert's Army of Ireland, 1,100 strong, sails from Rochefort in three frigates, taking a circuitous route to avoid detection by the English navy.

August 22:
French forces land at Cill Chuimín, Co. Mayo and capture Cill Ala. Irish insurgents join them.

August 23-24:
The Franco-Irish Army captures Ballina. The three frigates return to France.

August 25-26:
Cornwallis, the Lord Lieutenant, takes the field and sends an urgent request for reinforcements to England. Generals Lake, Hutchinson and Trench reinforce Castlebar, the major garrison town of North Connacht, against possible attack.

August 26-27:
Humbert leaves 200 men to protect Cill Ala and takes 1,500 French and Irish troops on a forced march across the mountains to the west of Loch Con and descends "aniar aduaidh" on Castlebar from the Bearna Gaoithe.

August 27:
At 6.00 a.m. the English are surprised and outmanoeuvred at Castlebar. By mid-day the town is liberated and 11 big guns and huge supplies captured. The English flee to Hollymount and Tuam and some as far as Athlone, in what Thomas Pakenham in "The Year of Liberty" calls "one of the most ignominious defeats in British military history" and what the Irish have since called the "Races of Castlebar". Humbert sends a report to France and asks for immediate reinforcements.

August 28:
The English garrison evacuates Foxford and retreats to Boyle. Insurgents seize Westport, Newport, Ballinrobe, Swinford and Hollymount. Claremorris has already been taken. Cornwallis has arrived in Athlone but decides not to counterattack until he has assembled a massive army.

August 31:
Humbert, having extended his bridgehead, proclaims a Republic of Connacht, sets up a civil administration and trains more Irish recruits, including many who have defected from the Longford and Kilkenny Militias. He is recognised as a strict disciplinarian.

September 3-4:
The English retake Hollymount and prepare for a dawn attack on Castlebar. Humbert has anticipated this and evacuates Castlebar under cover of darkness, taking his army, now totalling 3,000 men, towards Sligo, covering 58 miles in 36 hours. The long march has begun. Some Irish troops under French officers remain to protect Cill Ala and receive the expected reinforcements.

Bliain na bhFrancach

songs of 1798

The Year of the French

C.MacC.

Irish Freedom Press – Cló Saoirse
223 Parnell Street, Dublin 1, Ireland
Tel: (01) 872 9747   Fax: (01) 872 9757
e-mail: saoirse@iol.ie

BRIAN Ó hUIGINN

September 5:

An English army from Sligo under Col. Vereker attacks the Franco-Irish army at Collooney. Humbert again outmanoeuvres them, Bartholomew Teeling shows outstanding bravery and the English retreat with heavy losses as far as Ballyshannon, Co. Donegal.

Cornwallis has now divided his army in two, one half under General Lake to pursue the enemy and the other half, under his own personal command, to protect the line of the river Shannon. The French and Irish "must not cross".

Meanwhile, the United Irishmen of Longford and Westmeath have assembled. They capture Wilson's Hospital near Mullingar but fail to take the town of Granard. Humbert, on hearing of the midlands rising decides to link up with the insurgents there. He is now near Manorhamilton but changes direction and goes straight for Granard. He abandons some of the heavier guns so as to make more speed. So far he has eluded the cordon closing in around him. With some luck he hopes to slip past the net, reach Granard and then strike for Dublin which is virtually unprotected as most of the garrison have been moved to Connacht.

September 6:

The Franco-Irish army reaches Drumkeerin in the evening. An envoy from Lord Cornwallis offers terms for surrender but they are rejected.

September 7:

Shortly before noon Humbert's army crosses the Shannon at Ballintra Bridge just south of Loch Allen, but they fail in an attempt to demolish the bridge behind them. His army shows signs of fatigue and skirmishes with the English advance guard become more frequent. The race for Granard quickens.

The Franco-Irish army reaches Cloone, in South Leitrim, while Cornwallis, with 15,000 men is at Mohill, five miles away. Humbert gets news that he is surrounded and outnumbered but decides to push on even if the best he can now do is to make a token resistance before surrender.

September 8:

Cornwallis has got ahead and blocks the road to Granard at Ballinalee, while General Lake's army attacks from the rear. This is the Battle of Ballinamuck, Co. Longford. The French surrender after a fight of half an hour and are treated as prisoners of war. Five hundred Irish are massacred, while 1,000 escape. More are hanged at Longford, Ballinalee, and Carrick-on-Shannon. General George Blake of Garracloon, Co. Mayo, Commander-in-Chief of the Irish Insurgent Battalions and Gunner James Magee are among those hanged near the battlefield.

September 21-23:

General Trench heads a three-pronged attack on Cill Ala. On Sunday, the 23rd, the last stand is made by the insurgents, and 300 of them die, most of them being indiscriminately sabred by the dragoons at the spot still known as "casán an áir".

A magnificent pyramid-like monument at French Hill, three miles south of Castlebar, marks the spot where a party of French cavalry, travelling under a flag of truce, were treacherously murdered by English forces. It was erected in 1876 and could be said to commemorate all of the 200 or so French soldiers who died for Irish freedom, mostly at Castlebar and Collooney. The inscription reads:

"In grateful remembrance of the gallant French soldiers who died fighting for the freedom of Ireland on the 27th August, 1798. They shall be remembered forever".

The Men of The West

(Air: Eoghan Cóir)

While you honour in song and in story the names of the patriot men,
Whose valour has covered with glory full many a mountain and glen,
Forget not the boys of the heather, who marshalled their bravest and best,
When Éire was broken in Wexford, and looked for revenge to the West.

Chorus

I give you the gallant old West, boys,
    Where rallied our bravest and best
When Ireland lay broken and bleeding;
    Hurrah for the men of the West!

The hilltops with glory were glowing, 'twas the eve of a bright harvest day,
When the ships we'd been wearily waiting sailed into Killala's broad bay;
And over the hills went the slogan, to waken in every breast
The fire that has never been quenched, boys, among the true hearts of the West.

Chorus

Killala was ours ere the midnight, and high over Ballina town
Our banners in triumph were waving before the next sun had gone down.
We gathered to speed the good work, boys, the true men anear and afar;
And history can tell how we routed the redcoats through old Castlebar.

Chorus

And pledge we "The stout sons of France," boys, bold Humbert and all his brave men,
Whose tramp, like the trumpet of battle, brought hope to the drooping again.
Since Éire has caught to her bosom on many a mountain and hill
The gallants who fell so they're here, boys, to cheer us to victory still.

Chorus

Though all the bright dreamings we cherished went down in disaster and woe,
The spirit of old is still with us that never would bend to the foe;
And Connacht is ready whenever the loud rolling tuck of the drum
Rings out to awaken the echoes and tell us the morning has come.

Chorus

So here's to the gallant old West, boys,
    Which rallied her bravest and best
When Ireland was broken and bleeding;
    Hurrah, boys! Hurrah for the West!

William Rooney

4

Muintir an Iarthair

(Fonn: Eoghan Cóir)

*Conchúr Mag Uidhir, dochtúir leighis, a d'aistrigh an t-amhrán bríomhar úd
"The Men of the West" le Liam Ó Maolruanaidh. Bhuaigh sé duais ag
Feis Mhaigh Eo, 1903.*

Má mholtar le scéal is le hamhrán,
Na fir a bhí tréan agus fíor,
Chuir clú agus cáil lena ndánacht
Ar ghleann agus sruthán 's sliabh.
Ná fágaig' ar deireadh na tréan-fhir
Do chruinnigh ar phlánaí Mhaigh Eo,
Nuair a ghnóthaigh na Gaill i Loch Garman —
Siad muintir an Iarthair 'bhí beo!

Curfá
Seo sláinte na bhfear as an Iarthar díbh,
Do chruinnigh le cúnamh san ár!
Sheas siad in aimsir an ghéar-chaill —
Seo sláinte fear Chonnacht go bráth!

Tháinig na longa lá Fómhair,
Go cuan Chill Ala ag snámh,
'S bhíomar chomh fada ag súil leo
Gur shíleamar nach dtiocfadh go bráth.
Agus thosaigh na hadharca ag séideadh,
Ag fógairt go raibh siad ar fáil,
Agus corraíodh spreacadh in Éirinn
Nach múchfar i gConnacht go bráth!

Curfá

Níor bhuail sé an dó dhéag san oíche
Gur ghlan'mar Cill Ala go breá;
'S ní dheachaidh an ghrian síos 'na dhiaidh sin
Go raibh brat glas ar chúirt Bhéal an Átha.
Chruinnigh na céadta le cúnamh,
Agus mairfidh an scéal sin go buan;
An chaoi 'raibh na redcoats á ruaigeadh
As Caisleán an Bharraigh go Tuaim.

Curfá

5

Agus goirim na Francaigh bhreá' láidre
Do tháinig le Humbert anall,
Mar thug siad dúinn croí agus misneach
Nuair a bhíomar go brónach sa ngábh!
Agus trócaire Dé ar na céadta
Do thit 's do leagadh san ár,
Tá a gcnámha faoi fhód glas na hÉireann
Agus cuimhneoimid orthu go brách!

Curfá

Má caitheadh le fána ár smaointe,
'S ár ndóchas faoi scrios agus léan,
Tá an fíor-spiorad beo inár gcroíthe
Nach ngéillfidh don námhaid go héag!
Agus féach! Táimid réidh ar an nóiméad
A chluinfimid torann an áir,
Ag fógairt ar chlanna na hÉireann
Go bhfuil saoirse ár n-oileáin ar fáil!

Curfá
Seo sláinte na gConnachtach fíora
Do chruinnigh le cúnamh san ár!
'Siad togha agus rogha na tíre;
Seo sláinte sean-Chonnacht go bráth!

William Rooney ("Fear na Muintire") of Dublin was the energetic organiser of the 1898 Centenary commemoration of 1798. He worked unceasingly as a writer and lecturer and, in the words of Brian O hUiginn he "blazed the trail to 1916 and gave his life for Ireland". He died in 1901.

6

The Weapons and the Men

Though the beauties of the summer
Decked green Erin's fertile breast,
There was woe and bitter wailing
In the valleys of the West.
For the presence of the tyrant
Cursed the mountain and the glen;
And the laggard Frenchman came not
With the weapons for our men.

But when autumn browned the cornfields
And the leaves upon the trees,
You could hear the rising murmur
Swell to thunder in the breeze.
Eyes that long were dimmed in slavery
Flashed with Freedom's light again
For the French were in Killala
With the weapons for our men!

It has come, the day of vengeance
That our souls have waited long;
Vengeance on the hated tyrant
For each dark and bitter wrong.
As the mountain fox is hunted
Back into his loathsome den,
So we'll scourge the brutal tyrant
With our weapons and our men.

James Stinson

7

The Sean-Bhean Bhocht

O! The French are on the sea,
    Says the sean-bhean bhocht;
The French are on the sea,
    Says the sean-bhean bhocht;
O! the French are in the bay,
They'll be here without delay,
And the Orange will decay,
    Says the sean-bhean bhocht.

    Chorus
    O! the French are in the bay,
    They'll be here by break of day,
    And the Orange will decay,
        Says the sean-bhean bhocht.

And their camp it shall be where?
    Says the sean-bhean bhocht;
Their camp it shall be where?
    Says the sean-bhean bhocht;
On the Currach of Kildare,
The boys they will be there,
With their pikes in good repair,
    Says the sean-bhean bhocht.

    To the Currach of Kildare
    The boys will they repair,
    And Lord Edward will be there,
        Says the sean-bhean bhocht.

Then what will the yeomen do?
    Says the sean-bhean bhocht;
What will the yeomen do?
    Says the sean-bhean bhocht;
What should the yeomen do
But throw off the red and blue,
And swear that they'll be true
To the sean-bhean bhocht?

    What should the yeomen do
    But throw off the red and blue,
    And swear that they'll be true
    To the sean-bhean bhocht?

And what colour will they wear?
    Says the sean-bhean bhocht;
What colour will they wear?
    Says the sean-bhean bhocht;
What colour should be seen
Where our fathers' homes have been,
But our own immortal Green?
    Says the sean-bhean bhocht.

    What colour should be seen
    Where our fathers' homes have been,
    But our own immortal Green?
        Says the sean-bhean bhocht.

And will Ireland then be free?
    Says the sean-bhean bhocht;
Will Ireland then be free?
    Says the sean-bhean bhocht;
Yes! Ireland SHALL be free,
From the centre to the sea;
Then hurrah! for Liberty!
    Says the sean-bhean bhocht.

    Yes! Ireland SHALL be free,
    From the centre to the sea;
    Then hurrah! for Liberty!
        Says the sean-bhean bhocht.

C.MacC.

9

An tSean-Bhean Bhocht

"Tá na Francaigh teacht thar sáile"
    Ars an tSean-bhean bhocht.
"Tá na Francaigh teacht thar sáile,"
    Ars an tSean-bhean bhocht
"Táid ag teacht le soilse ré,
Beid anseo le fáinne an lae,
'S beidh ár námhaid go cráite tréith,"
    Ars an tSean-bhean bhocht.

"Is cá mbeidh cruinniú na Féinne?"
    Ars an tSean-bhean bhocht.
"Is cá mbeidh cruinniú na Féinne?"
    Ars an tSean-bhean bhocht.
"Thíos ar bhánta leathan réidh,
Cois Chill Dara ghrámhar shéimh,
Pící glana 's claímhte faobhair,"
    Ars an tSean-bhean bhocht.

"Is a bhfaighimid fós ár saoirse?"
    Ars an tSean-bhean bhocht.
"Is an bhfaighimid fós ár saoirse?"
    Ars an tSean-bhean bhocht.
"Beimid saor 'dir bhun is craobh,
Beimid saor ó thaobh go taobh,
Saor go deo le cabhair na naomh!"
    Ars an tSean-bhean bhocht.

Mícheál Ó Súilleabháin a d'aistrigh

The Croppy Boy

(Air: Cailín Óg a Stór)

*In the 1790s Irish Republicans began to crop their hair short in the
new French fashion. Hence the name "Croppy".*

"Good men and true in this house who dwell,
To a stranger buachaill I pray you tell,
Is the priest at home, or may he be seen?
I would speak a word with Father Green."

"The priest's at home, boy, and may be seen;
'Tis easy speaking with Father Green;
But you must wait till I go and see
If the holy father alone may be."

The youth has entered a silent hall —
What a lonely sound has his light footfall!
And the gloomy chamber's chill and bare,
With a vested priest in a lonely chair.

The youth has knelt to tell his sins.
"Nomine Dei," the youth begins;
At "Mea culpa" he beats his breast,
And in broken murmurs he speaks the rest.

"At the siege of Ross did my father fall,
And at Gorey my loving brothers all,
I alone am left of my name and race,
I will go to Wexford and take their place.

"I cursed three times since last Easter Day —
As Mass-time once I went to play,
I passed the churchyard one day in haste
And forgot to pray for my mother's rest.

"I bear no hate against living thing,
But I love my country above the King.
Now, Father, bless me and let me go
To die if God has ordained it so."

11

The priest said naught, but a rustling noise
Made the youth look up in wild surprise:
The robes were off, and in scarlet there
Sat a Yeoman captain with fiery glare.

With fiery glare and with fury hoarse,
Instead of a blessing he breathed a curse:
"'Twas a good thought, boy, to come here and shrive,
For one short hour is your time to live.

"Upon yon river three tenders float,
The priest's in one — if he isn't shot —
We hold this house for our lord the King,
And, Amen, say I, may all traitors swing!"

At Geneva Barracks that young man died,
And at Passage they had his body laid.
Good people, who live in peace and joy,
Breathe a prayer, shed a tear, for the Croppy Boy.

Carroll Malone

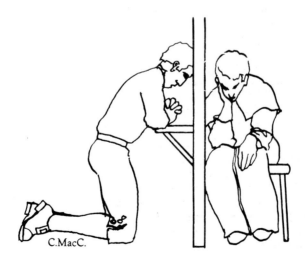

C.MacC.

Kelly of Killanne

John Kelly of Killanne, Co. Wexford was detailed by the Commander-in-Chief, Bagenal Harvey, to bring in all the available men from the Barony of Bantry for the attack planned on New Ross. He was seriously wounded in Michael Street, New Ross, following the successful attack on Three Bullet Gate. He was recovering in Wexford Town when it was recaptured by the British. A Yeoman sergeant who was a neighbour and whose life he had saved some days before, gave evidence against him. He was hanged on Wexford Bridge, his trunk conveyed to the waters and his head trailed and kicked along the streets before being spiked. Friends recovered the head and brought it to Killanne for burial and a monument was later erected on the spot.

The farmers of East Shelmalier were accustomed to shoot wild fowl on the North sloblands. Their "long barrelled guns" proved to be very effective weapons during the Rising.

What's the news? What's the news? O my bold Shelmalier,
    With your long-barrelled gun of the sea?
Say what wind from the south blows his messenger here
    With a hymn of the dawn for the free?
"Goodly news, goodly news, do I bring, Youth of Forth;
    Goodly news shall you hear, Bargy man!
For the boys march at morn from the South to the North,
    Led by Kelly, the Boy from Killanne!"

"Tell me who is that giant with gold curling hair —
    He who rides at the head of your band?
Seven feet is his height, with some inches to spare,
    And he looks like a king in command!" —
"Ah, my lads, that's the pride of the bold Shelmaliers,
    'Mong our greatest of heroes, a Man! —
Fling your beavers aloft and give three ringing cheers
    For John Kelly, the Boy from Killanne!"

Enniscorthy's in flames, and old Wexford is won,
    And the Barrow tomorrow we·cross,
On a hill o'er the town we have planted a gun
    That will batter the gateways of Ross!
All the Forth men and Bargy men march o'er the heath,
    With brave Harvey to lead on the van;
But the foremost of all in the grim Gap of Death
    Will be Kelly, the Boy from Killanne!"

But the gold sun of Freedom grew darkened at Ross,
   And it set by the Slaney's red waves;
And poor Wexford, stript naked, hung high on a cross,
   And her heart pierced by traitors and slaves!
Glory O! Glory O! to her brave sons who died
   For the cause of long-down-trodden man!
Glory O! to Mount Leinster's own darling and pride —
   Dauntless Kelly, the Boy from Killanne!"

P. J. McCall

Patrick Joseph McCall (1861-1919) was born in Patrick Street, Dublin. His summer holidays were spent in Rathangan, Co. Wexford, where he made the acquaintance of local musicians and ballad singers. He collected many old Irish airs, but is best remembered for his patriotic ballads.

L'année des Français

During the week following the liberation of Castlebar, even some of the French soldiers wrote verses. Here are two samples. The first is a somewhat humorous comment on the habit of their Commander of riding along the Irish ranks, raising his sword and shouting "Éirinn go brách". That was probably the only Irish he knew, and since most of the insurgents spoke only Irish, they understood him well.

L'incomparable Humbert si fécond en idées
De ce cri d'allégresse adopta le refrain.

En passant dans les rangs, on le voyait soudain
Chanter et répéter ces sublimes pensées:
Amis, Éirinn go brách! marchons à la victoire.
Amis, Éirinn go brách! va nous couvrir de gloire.

— Par Sous-lieutenant Fauré

Éirinn go brách! Fut le cri d'allégresse
Éirinn go brách! Fut le cri des combats
Éirinn go brách! Fut le cri de tristesse
Éirinn go brách! Fut celui du trépas.

— Par Sous-lieutenant Thibaut,
officier payeur de l'armée.

Mise 'gus Tusa

Rann do Pháistí, a cumadh i 1798.

An raibh tú 'g Cill Ala,
Nó i gCaisleán an Bharraigh,
Nó'n bhfaca tú 'n campa
'Bhí age na Francaigh?
Mise 'gus tusa 'gus ruball na muice
'Gus bacaigh Shíol Aindí, bacaigh Shíol Aindí.*

Do bhí mé 'g Cill Ala
'S i gCaisleán an Bharraigh
'S do chonaic mé 'n campa
'Bhí age na Francaigh.
Mise 'gus tusa 7rl.

An raibh tú 'r a' gCruach,
Nó 'n bhfaca tú 'n slua
Do bhí ar Chruach Phádraic
'Bhí ar Chruach Phádraic?
Mise 'gus tusa 7rl.

Do bhí mé 'r a' gCruach
'S do chonaic mé 'n slua
Do bhí ar Chruach Phádraic
'Bhí ar Chruach Phádraic
Mise 'gus tusa 7rl.

Ón mBéaloideas

---

* *Bhí reisimintí Albanacha ag na Sasanaigh i Maigh Eo i*
  1798. Is cosúil go dtagann "bacaigh Shíol Aindí" ó
  "Bucky Heelander" an Bhéarla.

15

La Marseillaise

*This marching song of the French Army of the Revolution
has since become the National Anthem of France.*

Allons enfants de la Patrie,
Le jour de gloire est arrivé;
Contre nous, de la tyrannie
L'étendard sanglant est levé,
L'étendard sanglant est levé.
Entendez-vous dans les campagnes
Mugir ces féroces soldats?
Ils viennent jusque dans nos bras
Égorger nos fils, nos compagnes.

> Aux armes, Citoyens!
> Formez vos bataillons!
> Marchons!
> Marchons!
> Qu'un sang impur abreuve nos sillons.

Amour sacré de la Patrie
Conduis, soutiens nos bras vengeurs
Liberté, Liberté chérie,
Combats avec tes défenseurs; (bis)
Sous nos drapeaux, que la Victoire
Accoure à tes mâles accents,
Que tes ennemis expirants
Voient notre triomphe et votre gloire.

> Aux armes, Citoyens!
> Formez vos bataillons!
> Marchons!
> Marchons!
> Qu'un sang impur abreuve nos sillons.

Rouget de Lisle (1792)

The Memory of the Dead

*This song was written in 1843, when the author was a
20-year-old student in Trinity College, Dublin.*

Who fears to speak of 'Ninety-eight?
    Who blushes at the name?
When cowards mock the patriot's fate,
    Who hangs his head for shame?
He's all a knave, or half a slave,
    Who slights his country thus:
But a *true* man, like you, man,
    Will fill your glass with us.

We drink the memory of the brave,
    The faithful and the few —
Some lie far off beyond the wave,
    Some sleep in Ireland, too;
All — all are gone — but still lives on
    The fame of those who died;
All true men, like you, men,
    Remember them with pride.

Some on the shores of distant lands,
    Their weary hearts have laid;
And by the stranger's heedless hands,
    Their lonely graves were made.
But though their clay be far away
    Beyond the Atlantic foam —
In true men, like you, men,
    Their spirit's still at home.

The dust of some is Irish earth;
    Among their own they rest;
And the same land that gave them birth
    Has caught them to her breast.
And we will pray that from their clay
    Full many a race may start
Of true men, like you, men,
    To act as brave a part.

They rose in dark and evil days
    To right their native land;
They kindled there a living blaze
    That nothing can withstand.
Alas! That Might can vanquish Right —
    They fell and passed away
But true men, like you, men,
    Are plenty here today.

Then here's their memory — may it be
    For us a guiding light,
To cheer our strife for liberty,
    And teach us to unite
Through good and ill, be Ireland's still,
    Though sad as theirs your fate;
And true men, be you men,
    Like those of 'Ninety-eight.

John Kells Ingram

Bás An Chroipí

Aithriseoireacht

Sínte ar thaobh an tsléibhe
    Chonaic mé an Croipí bocht;
Bhí an drúcht go trom ar a éadan,
    Bhí piléar trína ucht.

Bhí sé i bhfad óna chairde,
    I bhfad óna theach is a mhnaoi;
Agus é ina aonar fágtha
    Ar an bhféar fuar fliuch 'na luí.

Sa bhotháinín sléibhe
    Bhí bean ag gol is ag caoi,
Ag caoineadh ar son a céile
    Nach dtiocfadh ar ais a choích'.

"A mháthair, ná bí ag caoineadh,
    Ná bí ag briseadh do chroí,
Ní fada go bhfillfidh Daidí,
    Suigh síos agus lig do scíth."

"Ní fhéadaim, a mhic, ní fhéadaim,
    Tá cnapán mór i m'ucht,
B'fhéidir gur páiste gan athair
    Tú féin, a mhic, anocht."

"A mháthair, tá Dia cineálta,
    Ní ligfidh sé dochar dó;
Ná habair, ná habair, a mháthair
    Ná habair nach bhfuil sé beo."

Ach d'fhan sé san áit inar thit sé,
    Agus piléar trína ucht;
Nach silfidh Éire aon deoirín
    Ar son a saighdiúr' bhoicht?

Dúghlas de hÍde (An Craoibhín)

C.MacC.

19

Rouse, Hibernians

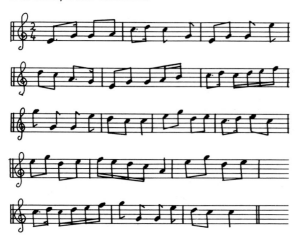

Rouse, Hibernians, from your slumbers!
See the moment just arrived
Imperious tyrants for to humble
Our French brethren are at hand.

Chorus
Vive la,* United heroes,
Triumphant always may they be,
Vive la, our gallant brethren
That have come to set us free.

Erin's sons, be not faint-hearted
Welcome, sing then "Ça ira",**
From Killala they are marching
To the tune of "Vive la".

Chorus

To arms quickly, and be ready,
Join the ranks and never flee,
Determined stand by one another
And from tyrants you'll be free.

Chorus

Cruel tyrants who oppressed you,
Now with terrors see their fall!
Then bless the heroes who caress you,
The Orange now goes to the wall.

Chorus

Apostate Orange, why so dull now?
Self-willed slaves, why do you frown?
Sure you might know how Irish freemen
Soon would put your Orange down.

Chorus

* Pronounced here "viva la". It comes from the slogan "vive la liberté".
** A marching song of the French Army of the Revolution, like the Marseillaise.

An Caiptín Máilleach

Moladh ar an gCaiptín Séamas Bán Ó Máille as Cnoc Mhuire, Co. Mhaigh Eo.
Ghlac sé páirt san Éirí Amach agus crochadh é ina dhiaidh sin.

Is mise Caiptín Máilleach,
Fear claímhe, píc' is láige,
Fear cneasta, gnaíúil grámhar
    Ar aonach, damhs' nó spóirt.
Is mé a sheasfadh dána
I mbearnain bhaoil le háthas
Ar ceart dom' bhuín 's mo chairde
    Dá mba 'ndán dom an róp.

Ceal airm, dín nó éide
I ngleannta doimhne 's sléibhte
Chleachtaigh muid fian-réiteach
    Do thíocht na bhFrancach cróga;
I mBeárnain mhaol na Gaoithe
Sa gCaistilbeár na dhéigh sin
Ruaig muid na Breathnaigh bhréagach'
    Is ár bpíce len a dtóin!

Ach! anois tá mo chnaipe déanta,
Go bhfóire an Tríonóid Naofa 'rm,
An Mhaighdean gheal 's a hAon-Mhac
    Go dtarrthaí mé go deo.
Mar is mise an Caiptín Máilleach
Fear ceart de chineál Gráinne,
Fear tíre nó fear sáile,
    Fear troda, siams' nó spóirt.

Mo mhallacht ar an mBrúnach
Mark Grady is a chúmplacht,
Na Diolúnaigh is na Diúcaigh,
    Is na Dáibhisigh bréana fós;
Bhíodh ár scrios 's ár sciúirse
Ó Swinford go Cúl Luachra,
Ó Scrig go Tullaigh Luachra
    Na middlemen 's na Yeos.

Páid O'Donoghue

One of the favourite recitations of P. H. Pearse

The Yeos were in Dunshaughlin, and the Hessians in Dunreagh,
    And spread thro' fair Moynalty were the Fencibles of Reagh,
While Roden's godless troopers ranged from Skreen to Mullachoo,
    When hammered were the pikeheads first by Páid O'Donoghue.

Young Páid, he was as brave a boy as ever hammer swung,
    And the finest hurler that you'd find the lads of Meath among;
And when the wrestling match was o'er no man could boast he threw
    The dark-haired smith of Curroghá, young Páid O'Donoghue.

So Pádraig lived a happy life and gaily sang each day
    Beside his ringing anvil some sweet old Irish lay,
Or roamed light-heartedly at eve thro' the woods of lone Kilbrue,
    With her who'd given her pure heart's love to Páid O'Donoghue.

But Ninety-Eight's dark season came and Irish hearts were sore;
    The pitch-cap and triangle the patient folk outwore;
The blacksmith thought of Ireland and found he'd work to do:
    "I'll forge some steel for freedom," said Páid O'Donoghue.

Tho' the Yeos were in Dunshaughlin and the Hessians in Dunreagh,
    Tho' spread thro' fair Moynalty were the Fencibles of Reagh;
Tho' Roden's godless troopers ranged from Skreen to Mullachoo,
    The pike-heads keen were hammered out by Páid O'Donoghue.

And so in Curroghá each night was heard the anvil's ring,
    While scouting on the roadways were Hugh and Phelim King,
With Gillic's Mat, and Duffy's Pat, and Mickey Gilsenan, too,
    While in the forge for Ireland worked young Páid O'Donoghue.

But a traitor crept amongst them, and the secret soon was sold
    To the captain of the Yeomen for the ready Saxon gold;
And a troop burst out one evening from the woods of dark Kilbrue,
    And soon a rebel prisoner bound, was Páid O'Donoghue.

Now Pádraig Og pray fervently, your earthly course has run;
    The captain he has sworn you'll not see the morrow's sun.
The muskets they are ready, and each yeoman's aim is true;
    Death stands beside thy shoulder, young Páid O'Donoghue.

"Down on your knees, you rebel dog," the yeoman captain roared,
  As high above his helmet's crest he waved his gleaming sword.
"Down on your knees to meet your doom, such is the rebel's due;"
  But straight as pike shaft 'fore him stood bold Páid O'Donoghue.

And there upon the roadway where in childhood he had played,
  Before the cruel yeoman he stood quite undismayed —
"I kneel but to my God above, I ne'er shall bow to you;
  You can shoot me as I'm standing," said Páid O'Donoghue.

The captain gazed in wonder, then lowered his keen edged blade,
  "A rebel bold as this," he said "'tis fitting to degrade.
Here men!" he cried, "unbind him, my charger needs a shoe;
  The King shall have a workman in this Páid O'Donoghue."

Now to the forge young Páid has gone, the yeomen guard the door,
  And soon the ponderous bellows is heard to snort and roar;
The captain stands with reins in hand while Pádraig fits the shoe,
  And when 'tis on full short the shrift he'll give O'Donoghue.

The last strong nail is firmly clenched, the captain's horse is shod!
  Now rebel bold thine hour hath come, prepare to meet thy God!
But why holds he the horse's hoof there's no more work to do?
  Why clenches he his hammer so, young Páid O'Donoghue?

A leap! a roar! a smothered groan! the captain drops the rein,
  And sinks to earth with hammer-head sunk deeply in his brain;
And lightly in the saddle fast racing towards Kilbrue
  Upon the captain's charger sits bold Páid O'Donoghue.

A volley from the pistols, a rush of horses' feet —
  He's gone! and none can capture the captain's charger fleet;
And on the night wind backwards comes a mocking loud "Halloo!"
  That tells the yeomen they have lost young Páid O'Donoghue.

Young Páid fought at Tara, you know the nation's tale;
  Though borne down in that struggle, not hopeless is the Gael,
For still in Meath's fair county, there are brave lads — not a few
  Who would follow in the footsteps of bold Páid O'Donoghue.

Patrick Archer

Jean-Joseph Amable Humbert

Puisque ce militaire
Daigne guider nos pas,
Suivons Amable Humbert
Et ne le quittons pas.

— Chapeau de paille d'Italie
(Acte II, Sc. V,
Eugène La Biche)

General Humbert's expedition landed at Cill Chuimín, near Cill Ala on 22nd August 1798. They had sailed in three frigates from Rochefort, near La Rochelle, on 6th August. Their force consisted of 1,100 officers and men. They brought three light cannon and a considerable quantity of muskets, bayonets, pistols, sabres, ammunition, gun powder and uniforms. Within 24 hours 1,000 Irish insurgents had rallied to join them.

Humbert outclassed three English Generals at Castlebar on 27th August and captured the town from a vastly superior force. He proclaimed a Republic of Connacht and John Moore of Moore Hall was installed as President.

It took Lord Cornwallis and a force of about 30,000 men to defeat the Franco-Irish army at Ballinamuck, Co. Longford on 8th September. The second French force of 3,000 men, including Wolfe Tone, had been delayed at Brest and did not arrive until 12th October. They were intercepted and defeated by the British off the Donegal coast.

Humbert died in New Orleans in 1823 at the age of 55.

An Spailpín Fánach

Leagan Connachtach

Tá na Francaigh anois istigh i gCill Ala
Agus beimid go leathan láidir;
Tá Bonaparte i gCaisleán an Bharraigh
Ag iarraidh an dlí a cheap Sáirséal.
Beidh beairicí an rí ins gach aon-oíche trí lasadh
Agus yeomen againn ar garda,
Puiceanna an Bhéarla go síorraí dá leagan —
Sin cabhair ag an Spailpín Fánach.

B'fhaide liom lá a bheinn i dtír gan chara
Ná bliain mhór fhada is ráithe,
Ag baint na díogan is dá síor-chartadh
Go dté an ghrian ina háras.
Glacfad fís ó rí na gCraipí;
Beidh spíc agus cleith ins gach láimh liom;
Agus ar an tsráid seo arís ní ghlaofar m'ainm —
Cá gcónaíonn an Spailpín Fánach?

In Inis a bhíos is mo chúl le balla
Agus arís go dtí lá 'r na mhárach.
Mná na leannta ag glaoch isteach orm,
Súil is go n-ólfainn mo phá(ighe).
Tháinig mé isteach is deamhan pingin a bhí i mo bhealach
Agus mé go leathan láidir;
Is deamhan cárt dí a gheobhainn ar m'fhocal —
Mar bhí mé 'mo Spailpín Fánach.

Is d'ardaigh mé mo láí liom suas go Gaillimh
Is mé ag gabháil ag saothrú pá(ighe),
I gContae an Rí ba mhian liom seasamh
Ach ní bhfaighinn ann bia ná pá(ighe).
Ar chuanta Bh'l' Áth Cliath a liath mo phlaite
Is nárbh é sin an t-aistear náireach?
Ach i measc mo ghaolta, pósfaidh mé feasta —
Is ní bheidh mé 'mo Spailpín Fánach.

Henry Joy

(Air: The same as "The Singing Bird" and is often played in Croke Park by the Artane Boys' Band)

Henry Joy McCracken was born in High Street, Belfast, in 1767. A member of one of the most notable Presbyterian commercial families in that city, he joined the Society of United Irishmen and led the Republican forces when they captured Antrim town from the British garrison in 1798. Arrested after the insurrection, he was courtmartialled and hanged in the Cornmarket, Belfast, on the evening of July 17th, 1798. His sister Mary Ann walked arm-in-arm with him to the gallows. This Belfast street ballad was written about 1800.

An Ulster man I am proud to be,
From the Antrim glens I come.
Although I labour by the sea,
I have followed flag and drum.
I have heard the martial tramp of men;
I've seen them fight and die.
Ah! lads I well remember when
I followed Henry Joy.

I pulled my boat in from the sea,
    I hid my sails away.
I hung my nets upon a tree
    And scanned the moonlit bay.
The boys were out, the redcoats too,
    I bade my wife good-bye,
And then beneath the greenwood glade
    I followed Henry Joy.

Alas, for Ireland's cause we fought
    For home and sire we bled.
Though our arms were few, our hearts beat true
    And five to one lay dead.
And many a lassie missed her lad
    And mother mourned her boy,
For youth was strong in the dashing throng
    That followed Henry Joy.

In Belfast town they built a tree
    And the redcoats mustered there.
I watched him come as the roll of the drum
    Sounded on the barrack square.
He kissed his sister, went aloft
    Then waved a last good-bye,
And as he died, I turned and cried
    They have murdered Henry Joy.

The Battle of Granard

(Air: "The Rising of the Moon")

Down by Sheelin's vale at sunset,
    Fierce as demons in their wrath,
Spread a band of English troopers
    Fire and carnage marked their path.

Midnight shines, and blazing rooftree
    Lit the darkness of the night,
From the shores of fair Lough Gowna
    To the slopes of Granard's height.

Maid and mother fell before them,
    All in wrath and vengeance smote,
And in pride the foeman's legion
    Onward sped to Granard's Moat.

We marched that morn from Creenagh
    To oppose them on their way,
And by river, lake or mountain
    Made we neither stop or stay.

Till a band of English troopers
    Crossed our path at Edgeworthstown
And we piked the last red foeman
    As the evening sun went down.

Early in the dewy morning,
    As the day began to dawn
Towards the ancient moat of Granard
    We were proudly marching on.

High o'erhead us waved our banner
    In its beauty fair and free,
Borne by men from Carrickmoira
    And the plains of Killashee.

From the banks of Cloonart river
    And from Cleaney's village green,
Hast'ning onwards to the onset
    Many a gallant youth was seen.

As we reached the heights of Granard
    Right before us, formed in line,
We could see the English legion
    And their spears and banner shine.

For a moment's space we halted
    As we came within their view,
Then a deadly thirst for vengeance
    Filled our bosoms through and through.

With a shout that loudly echoed
    To the far-off Shannon shore,
Through the red ranks of the foeman
    In a furious rush we tore.

With that rush our gallant pikemen
    Leaped against their foremost line,
And their blades drank deep in vengeance
    For many a bloody crime.

Fast and deadly ev'ry weapon
    Found a Saxon foeman's breast,
As our fierce and maddened pikemen
    Through their columns thickly pressed.

Granard's ancient moat was reddened
    By the blood of friend and foe,
Well we met them with their bayonets
    With our pike their sabre-blow.

Backwards pressed against the valley
    Bravely fighting to the last,
But again our gallant pikemen
    Gathered round them fierce and fast.

Morning saw their haughty standard
    In its pride and glory wave;
Evening saw the foeman's legion
    Crushed and sunk in one red grave.

And where stood the ranks of Britain
    By the light of morning's dawn,
O'er their graves in proud defiance
    Erin's rebel banner shone.

Longford long shall tell the story,
How her children bravely stood
In that fight for Erin's glory
Brave and stern as freemen should.

And their deeds shall nerve their brothers
When they grasp the freeman's brand,
To go forth, to fall or conquer
For the rights of motherland.

Liberty, Equality, Fraternity, Union

"After several unsuccessful attempts, behold at last Frenchmen arrived amongst you...

"Brave Irishmen, our cause is common. Like you we hold as indefeasible the right of all nations to liberty. Like you we are persuaded that the peace of the world shall ever be troubled as long as the British ministry is suffered to make with impunity a traffic of the industry, labour and blood of the people...

"Union, Liberty, the Irish Republic! Such is our shout. Let us march. Our hearts are devoted to you; our glory is in your happiness".

From General Humbert's Proclamation
of 22nd August, 1798

Sliabh na mBan

Ní airím véarsa ó lon ná ó chéirseach
Is ní fhásann féar ins na coillte ceart';
Níl suim ag an spéirbhean i spórt ná i bpléisiúr
Ach í ag gol is ag béiceadh is ag réabadh bas.
Á rá gan faothamh, ní bhfaighidh na séimhfhir
Aon oíche in Éirinn ná uain chun reast,
Ag an trúp seo meirligh is iad ag teacht lena chéile,
Is go mbuailfear caoch sinn ar Shliabh na mBan.

Is is oth liom féinig bualadh an lae úd
Do dhul ar Ghaeil bhocht 'is na céadta slad;
Mar tá na meirligh ag déanamh géim dínn,
Is a rá nach aon ní leo píc ná sleá.
Níor tháinig ár major i dtús an lae chughainn,
Is ní rabhamar féinig i gcóir ná i gceart,
Ach mar a sheolfaí tréada de bha gan aoire
Ar thaobh na gréine de Shliabh na mBan.

Mo léan léir ar an dream gan éifeacht
Nár fhan le héirim istoíche is stad,
Go mbeadh dúthaí Déiseach is iarthar Éireann
Ag teacht lena chéile ón tír aneas.
Go mbeadh ár gcampaí déanta le fórsaí tréana,
Bheadh cúnamh Dé lirn is an saol ar fad,
Is ní dhíolfadh meirleach darbh ainm Néill sinn
Is bhuafaí an réim linn ar Shliabh na mBan.

Is é Ros do bhreoigh is do chloígh go deo sinn,
Mar ar fágadh mórchuid dínn sínte lag;
Leanaí óga 'na smóla dóite
Is an méid a fhan beo dhíobh cois claí nó scairt;
Ach geallaim féin díbh an té dhein an foghla,
Go mbeamna i gcóir dó le píc is le sleá,
Is go gcuirfeam yeomen ar crith 'na mbróga,
Ag díol a gcomhair leo ar Shliabh na mBan.

Tá na cóbaigh mhóra ag iarraidh eolais,
Tá an aimsir óg is an chabhair ag teacht;
An Té mhill na gnótha is É a leigheasfaidh fós iad,
Is ní dhíolfam feoirling leo, cíos ná sleá.
Píosa corónach, an chuid ba mhó dhe,
Luach éiric bó nó teaghlach deas,
Beidh rince ar bhóithre is soilse á ndó 'gainn,
Beidh meidhir is mórtas ar Shliabh na mBan.

Is mó fear aosta is crobhaire gléigeal,
Ó am go chéile a chuaigh thar lear,
A bhfuil córdaí caola ag baint lúth a ngéag díobh,
I ndoinsiúin dhaora go doimhin faoi ghlas;
Gardaí taobh leo ná leomhfadh sméid' orthu,
Do dhéanfadh plé dóibh i dtíortha thar lear;
Á dtabhairt saor óna namhaid gan bhuíochas,
In am an tsaothair ar Shliabh na mBan.

Is tá an Francach faobhrach is a loingeas gléasta,
Le cranna géara acu ar muir le seal;
'Sé an síorscéal go bhfuil a dtriall ar Éirinn,
Is go gcuirfid Gaeil bhocht' arís 'na gceart.
Dá mba dhóigh liom féinig go mb'fhíor an scéal úd,
Bheadh mo chroí chomh héadrom le lon ar sceach,
Go mbeadh cloí ar mheirligh is an adharc á séideach,
Ar thaobh na gréine de Shliabh na mBan.

Seo é leagan Béarla ar an véarsa deireanach:

For on the ocean are ships in motion,
And glad devotion on France's shore,
And rumour's telling; "they'll now be sailing
To help the Gael in the Right once more."
O! if true's that story, by my hopes of glory,
Like the glad bird o'er me I'll lilt my rann!
Were the robber routed! the Saxon flouted!
How we would shout it, old Sliabh na mBan!

The Croppy Boy

It was early early in the spring,
The birds did whistle and sweetly sing,
Changing their notes from tree to tree,
And the song they sang was old Ireland free.

It was early early last Tuesday night,
The yeoman cavalry gave me a fright;
The yeoman cavalry was my downfall,
And taken was I by Lord Cornwall.

It was to the guard-house I then was led,
And in a parlour I was tried;
My sentence passed and my courage low
To New Geneva* I was forced to go.

As I was passing my father's door,
My brother William stood at the door;
My aged father stood at the door,
And my tender mother her hair she tore.

As I was walking up Wexford Street
My own first cousin I chanced to meet;
My own first cousin did me betray,
And for one bare guinea swore my life away.

My sister Mary heard the express,
She ran upstairs in her morning-dress —
Five hundred guineas she would lay down,
To see me liberated in Wexford Town.

As I was walking up Wexford Hill,
Who could blame me to cry my fill?
I looked behind and I looked before,
But my tender mother I shall ne'er see more.

As I was mounted on the platform high,
My aged father was standing by;
My aged father did me deny,
And the name he gave me was the Croppy Boy.

It was in Geneva this young man died,
And in Geneva his body lies;
All you good Christians that do pass by
Breathe a prayer, shed a tear for the Croppy Boy.

Street Ballad

* *The British had a prison at New Geneva, or Geneva Barracks,
near Passage, Co. Waterford.*

35

'Ninety-Eight

A Centenary Ode, 1898.

Still forms, grey dust, black stones in Dublin city,
    A grave in green Kildare,
And many a grassy mound that moves our pity
    O'er Erin everywhere;

Cave Hill above the Lagan's noises rearing
    Her shaggy head in pride;
Lone Ednavady's brow and Antrim staring
    Across Lough Neagh's rough tide;

Killala still her weary watch maintaining
    Beside the ocean's boom,
And Castlebar in faithful guard remaining
    Around the Frenchmen's tomb.

Ross, Wexford, Gorey, Oulart, Tubberneering,
    And many a Wicklow glen
That knew the dauntless souls and hearts unfearing
    Of Dwyer and all his men —

These, through a hundred years of gloom and doubting
    Speak trumpet-toned to-day,
Above the cry of creed and faction's shouting
    To tread the olden way.

These, in the hearts of all the true men, waken
    The olden fires anew;
These tell of hope unquenched and faith unshaken,
    Of something still to do.

They bring us visions, full of tears and sorrow,
    Of homes and hearts left lone;
Of eyes grown dim with watching for a morrow
    Of joy that never shone.

But, too, they whisper notes of preparation
    And strength beyond the seas,
Of hope outliving night and desolation
    Through all the centuries.

Then to the staff-head let our flag ascending,
    Our fires on every hill
Tell to the nations of the earth attending
    We wage the battle still —

Tell to the nations, though the grass is o'er them,
    For many a weary year,
Our fathers' souls still thrill the land that bore them,
    Their spirit still is there.

And by their graves we swear this year of story
    To battle side by side,
Till Freedom crowns with immemorial glory
    The Cause for which they died.

William Rooney

Dublin Caſtle, 28th Auguſt, 1798.

IT appears by Advices received from the Honourable Major General *Hutchinſon,* dated *Caſtlebar,* 26th in the Evening, that the Enemy had not then attempted to move from *Killalla.* Their three Frigates had failed from the Coaſt. The Major General expected ſhortly to be in Force to move againſt the Enemy. The Province of *Connaught* continues in perfect Tranquillity.

DUBLIN: Printed by GEORGE GRIERSON, Printer to the KING's Moſt Excellent Majeſty.

Tone's Grave

In Bodenstown churchyard there is a green grave,
And wildly around it the winter winds rave;
Small shelter I ween are the ruined walls there
When the storm sweeps down on the plains of Kildare.
Once I lay on that sod — it lies over Wolfe Tone —
And thought how he perished in prison alone,
His friends unavenged and his country unfreed —
"Oh, bitter," I said, "is the patriot's meed.

"For in him the heart of a woman combined
With heroic spirit and a governing mind —
A martyr for Ireland, his grave has no stone —
His name seldom named, and his virtues unknown."
I was woke from my dream by the voices and tread
Of a band who came into the home of the dead;
They carried no corpse, and they carried no stone,
And they stopped when they came to the grave of Wolfe Tone.

There were students and peasants, the wise and the brave,
And an old man who knew him from cradle to grave,
And children who thought me hard-hearted, for they
On that sanctified sod were forbidden to play.
But the old man, who saw I was mourning there, said:
"We come, sir, to weep where young Wolfe Tone is laid,
And we're going to raise him a monument, too —
A plain one, yet fit for the loyal and true."

My heart overflowed, and I clasped his old hand,
And I blessed him, and blessed every one of his band:
"Sweet, sweet 'tis to find that such faith can remain
In the cause and the man so long vanquished and slain."
In Bodenstown churchyard there is a green grave,
And freely around it let winter winds rave —
Far better they suit him — the ruin and gloom —
Till Ireland, a nation, can build him a tomb.

Thomas Davis

Donncha Bán

Fuair Edward Bunting an t-amhrán seo i gCúige Chonnacht. Deirtear gur thaitin an fonn le Máire Nic Reachtain, deirfiúr Henry Joy McCracken, a crochadh freisin.

Is ar an mbaile seo chonaic sibh an t-ionadh
Ar Dhonncha Bán is é á dhaoradh,
Bhí caipín bán air in áit a hata,
Is róipín cnáibe in áit a charabhata.

Tá mé ag teacht ar feadh na hoíche
Mar bheadh uainín i measc seilbh mhóir caorach,
Mo bhrollach foscailte 's mo cheann liom scaoilte,
'S cá bhfaighinn mo dheartháirín romham ach sínte!

Chaoin mé an chéad dreas ag gob a' locha,
'S an dara dreas ag bun do chroiche,
An tríú dreas ag ceann do choirp-se,
I measc na nGall 's mo cheann á scoilteadh.

Dá mbeifeá agamsa san áit ar chóir duit,
Thíos i Sligeach nó i mBaile an Róba,
Bhrisfí an chroch, ghearrfaí an rópa,
'S ligfí Donncha Bán abhaile ar an eolas.

A Dhonncha Bháin níorbh é an chroch ba dhual duit,
Ach dul chuig an scioból 's d'easair a bhualadh,
An céachta d'iompú, deiseal 's tuathal
'S an taobh dhearg den fhód a chur in uachtar.

A Dhonncha Bháin, a dheartháirín dílis,
Is maith atá 's agam siúd a bhain díom thú;
Ag ól an chupáin, ag deargadh an phíopa
'S ag siúl an drúchta le com na hoíche.

A Mhic Uí Mhultháin, a sciúrsa an mhí-ádh
Ní lao bó bradaí a bhí in mo dheartháir,
Ach buachaillín cruinn-deas ar chnoc 's ar chnocán
A bhainfeadh fuaim go bog binn as camán.

39

'S a Dhonncha Bháin nach é sin an buaireadh
Agus 'fheabhas is d'iomprófá spoir is buatais!
Chuirfinn éadach faiseanta ort, den éadach ba bhuaine,
Agus chuirfinn amach thú mar mhac duine uasail.

A Mhic Uí Mhultháin! ná raibh do chlann mhac i bhfochair a chéile,
Ná do chlann iníon ag iarraidh spré ort!
Tá dhá cheann an chláir folamh, 's an t-urlár líonta,
Is Donncha Bán, mo dheartháirín, sínte.

Tá spré Dhonncha Bháin ag tíocht abhaile
Agus ní ba, caoirigh é ná capaill,
Ach tobac 's píopaí 's coinnle geala,
'S ní dá mhaíomh é ar lucht a gcaite.

Ón mBéaloideas

Dublin Caſtle, 29th *Auguſt,* 1798.

ADVICES were received laſt Night from Lieutenant
General *Lake,* by which it appears, that early on the
Morning of the 27th the *French* attacked him in his Po-
ſion near *Caſtlebar,* before his Force was aſſembled, and
compelled him, after a ſhort Action, to retire to *Holy-
mount.* The Lieutenant General regrets that ſix Field
Pieces fell into the Enemy's Hands; but ſtates that the
Loſs of the King's Troops, in Men, has not been conſi-
derable.

DUBLIN: Printed by GEORGE GRIERSON, Printer to the KING's Moſt Excellent Majeſty.

40

The Rising of the Moon

(Air: The Wearin' o' the Green)

Leo Casey (1846-1870) was proud of the efforts made by the United Irishmen of Longford and Westmeath in 1798. The "Singing River" is the Inny which flows into the Shannon from his native area between Mullingar and Ballymahon. He wrote many songs, including "Máire My Girl" and was active in the Fenian Brotherhood. By coincidence, his birthday was 22nd August, the same as General Humbert's and the date Humbert landed at Killala, in 1798. He died when he was only 23 as a result of the rigours of imprisonment. It is said that 50,000 people marched in his funeral procession in Dublin and that 150,000 more looked on. Thousands walked to Dublin from Longford, Westmeath and Roscommon to pay their respects.

Oh! then tell me, Seán O'Farrell,
    Tell me why you hurry so?
"Hush, mo bhuachaill, hush and listen,"
    And his cheeks were all aglow.
"I bear orders from the Captain,
    Get you ready quick and soon
For the pikes must be together
    By the rising of the moon."

Oh! then tell me, Seán O'Farrell,
    Where the gathering is to be?
"In the old spot by the river
    Right well known to you and me.
One word more — for signal token,
    Whistle up the marching tune,
With your pike upon your shoulder,
    By the rising of the moon."

Out from many a mud-wall cabin
    Eyes were watching through the night,
Many a manly breast was throbbing
    For the blessed warning light.
Murmurs passed along the valleys
    Like the Banshee's lonely croon,
And a thousand blades were flashing
    At the rising of the moon.

There beside the singing river
	That dark mass of men were seen;
Far above the shining weapons
	Hung their own beloved green.
"Death to every foe and traitor!
	Forward! strike the marching tune,
And hurrah, my boys, for freedom!
	'Tis the rising of the moon."

Well they fought for poor old Ireland,
	And full bitter was their fate
Oh! what glorious pride and sorrow
	Fill the name of 'Ninety-eight!
Yet, thank God, e'en still are beating
	Hearts in manhood's burning noon,
Who would follow in their footsteps
	At the rising of the moon!

John Keegan Casey (Leo)

C.MacC.

42

The Woman Cried

From humble home in dead of night,
A flitting shadow fled,
The yellow moon caught sharpened pike,
Where the night shades danced and played.

A bramble clawed at trembling hand,
And a night owl watched unseen,
Through bog and glen a United man,
Marched out to win a dream.

Cold black water lashed and splashed,
And played round a tattered reed,
By dying fire a woman prayed,
That the Gael might but succeed.

The silver nails of a rugged boot,
Scarred a lonely lifeless stone,
'Cross rambling hill he marched afoot
To fight along with Tone.

Six days he fought,
Midst dying piles of gory mutilated heroes,
And the English cannon roared.
Upon the ghosts of Celtic bones,
A nation's blood was poured.

Thousands fell in screaming bloody terror,
Whilst the informer hid cowering close by,
But there were none left amongst that bloody fray,
To hear the woman cry.

Bobby Sands

The author was the parliamentary representative for Fermanagh and South Tyrone when he died in the H-Blocks of Long Kesh Prison, on 5th May, 1981 after 66 days of hunger-strike.

The very last words of his diary, dated Tuesday 17th March, 1981, read as follows: "If they aren't able to destroy the desire for freedom, they won't break you. They won't break me because the desire for freedom, and the freedom of the Irish people, is in my heart. The day will dawn when all the people of Ireland will have the desire for freedom to show. It is then we'll see the rising of the moon."

'A short but very fatiguing campaign'

English historians have always treated General Humbert's expedition to Ireland with ridicule, but Brian Ó hUiginn was fond of quoting the military correspondent of the London *Times* who held a different view. This expert wrote some years ago:

"In these operations described by Cornwallis to the Duke of Portland as *a short but very fatiguing campaign,* a raiding party of 1,000 French landed in Ireland without opposition, after sixteen days of navigation, unobserved by the British Navy; defeated and drove back the British troops opposing them on four separate occasions; routed a force of second line troops of at least double its strength; captured eleven British guns; held the field for seventeen days; entirely occupied the attention of all the available troops of a garrison of Ireland 100,000 strong; penetrated almost to the centre of the island, and compelled the Lord Lieutenant to send an urgent requisition to London for 'as great a reinforcement as possible.'"

This was a fine tribute to General Humbert and his veteran troops who proved more than a match for the British army. No mention was made, however, of the substantial numbers of Irish insurgents who rallied to his flag and acquitted themselves well on the field of battle, particularly at Ballinamuck. They were mercilessly slaughtered, even after surrender, including Matthew Tone and Bartholomew Teeling, who held commissions in the French army.

The Man from God-Knows Where

A Recitation

Thomas Russell, of Co. Cork, bosom friend and devoted comrade of Tone and Emmet, organised Co. Down for the United Irishmen in 1795. One night he entered an inn or tavern in Killyleagh, where a number of local men were gathered. They were United Irishmen, but Russell didn't know it, and they didn't know him or why he was there. One of them, long years after, tells of that night, and tells where and under what circumstances he saw Russell again. The Warwick mentioned in the poem was a young Republican Presbyterian Minister who was hanged at Newtownards. Thomas Russell was hanged on 21st October, 1803.

Into our townlan', on a night of snow,
Rode a man from God-knows-where;
None of us bade him stay or go,
Nor deemed him friend, nor damned him foe.
But we stabled his big roan mare:
For in our townlan' we're a decent folk,
And if he didn't speak, why none of us spoke,
And we sat till the fire burned low.

We're a civil sort in our wee place,
So we made the circle wide
Round Andy Lemon's cheerful blaze,
And wished the man his lenth o' days;
And a good end to his ride,
He smiled in under his slouchy hat —
Says he: "There's a bit of a joke in that,
For we ride different ways."

The whiles we smoked we watched him
From his seat fornenst the glow,
I nudged Joe Moore, "You wouldn't dare
To ask him who he's for meetin' there,
And how far he has got to go?"
But Joe wouldn't dare, nor Wully Scott,
And he took no drink — neither cold nor hot —
This man from God-knows-where.

It was closin' time, an' late forbye,
When us ones braved the air —
I never saw worse (may I live or die)
Than the sleet that night, an' I says, says I,
"You'll find he's for stoppin' there."
But at screek o' day, through the gable pane
I watched him spur in the peltin' rain,
And I juked from his rovin' eye.

Two winters more, then the Trouble Year,
When the best that a man could feel
Was the pike he kept in hidlin's near,
Till the blood o' hate an' the blood o' fear
Would be redder nor rust on the steel.
Us ones quet from mindin' the farms —
Let them take what we gave wi' the weight o' our arms,
From Saintfield to Kilkeel.

In the time o' the Hurry, we had no lead —
We all of us fought with the rest —
An' if e'er a one shook like a tremblin' reed
None of us gave neither hint nor heed,
Nor ever even'd we'd guessed.
We men of the North had a word to say,
An' we said it then, in our own dour way,
An' we spoke as we thought was best.

All Ulster over, the weemen cried
For the stan'in' crops on the lan' —
Many's the sweetheart an' many's the bride
Would liefer ha' gone till where *he* died.
An ha' murned her lone by her man,
But us one weathered the thick of it,
And we used to dandher along, and sit
In Andy's side by side.

What with discoorse goin' to and fro,
The night would be wearin' thin,
Yet never so late when we rose to go
But someone would say: "Do ye min' thon snow,
An' the man what came wanderin' in?
And we be to fall to the talk again,
If by any chance he was *one o' them* —
The man who went like the win'.

46

C.MacC.

Well, 'twas gettin' on past the heat o' the year
When I rode to Newtown fair;
I sold as I could (the dealers were near —
Only three pound eight for the Innish steer,
An' nothin' at all for the mare!)
But I met McKee in the throng o' the street
Says he, "The grass has grown under our feet
Since they hanged young Warwick here."

And he told me that Boney had promised help
To a man in Dublin town
Says he, "If ye've laid the pike on the shelf,
Ye'd better go home hot-fut by yerself,
An' once more take it down."
So by Comer road I trotted the gray
And never cut corn until Killyleagh
Stood plain on the risin' groun'.

For a wheen o' days we sat waitin' the word
To rise and go at it like men,
But no French ships sailed into Cloughey Bay,
And we heard the black news on a harvest day
That the cause was lost again;
And Joey and me, and Wully Boy Scott,
We agreed to ourselves we'd as lief as not
Ha' been found in the thick o' the slain.

By Downpatrick Gaol I was bound to fare
On a day I'll remember, feth;
For when I came to the prison square
The people were waitin' in hundreds there,
An' you wouldn't hear stir nor breath!
For the sodgers were standin', grim an' tall,
Round a scaffold built there fornenst the wall,
An' a man stepped out for death!

I was brave an' near to the edge o' the throng,
Yet I knowed the face again,
An' I knowed the set, an' I knowed the walk
An' the sound of his strange up-country talk,
For he spoke out right an' plain.
Then he bowed his head to the swingin' rope,
While I said, "Please God" to his dying' hope
And "Amen" to his dyin' prayer.
That the Wrong would cease and the Right prevail.
For the man that they hanged at Downpatrick Gaol
Was the Man from God-knows-where!

Florence M. Wilson

47

An Gunnadóir Mac Aoidh

Aithriseoireacht

Tharla an eachtra seo le linn Chath Bhéal Átha na Muc i gCo. Longfoirt, 8ú Meán Fómhair 1798. Chroch na Sasanaigh Séamas Mac Aoidh i ndiaidh an chatha.

I mBaile na Muc, Dé Sathairn, chailleamar an lá,
Nuair a ghéill an ginearál Francach is a shaighdiúirí don námhaid.
Bhíomar féin ar Shean-mhullach os comhair arm mór an Rí.
"Go ndírí Dia an t-urchar," ars' an Gunnadóir Mac Aoidh.

Réab an liathróid iarainn a bealach tríd an aer;
Bhuail i measc an phúdair is séideadh é go spéir;
Is d'éirigh ceo an phléasctha gur chlúdaigh sé an ghrian:
"Mo ghrá go deo an t-iarann," ars' an Gunnadóir Mac Aoidh.

Ach b'shin an liathróid deiridh a bhí fágtha againn ar chlár;
Bhriseamar buicéidí, potaí, ciotail, cannaí stáin;
Baineadh tairní as bróga, cuireadh cnaipí ins an líon:
"Tá goile láidir ag an ngunna," ars' an Gunnadóir Mac Aoidh.

Briseadh carráiste beag an ghunna le hurchar na nGall;
Bhí an roth ina smidiríní, bhí an bairille ar sceabha,
Léimeadar chun gnímh, Taimí, Paidí agus Liam:
"Cuirigí na guaillí fúithi," ars' an Gunnadóir Mac Aoidh.

"Seo chugainn an Coirnéal Crawford," — chuir sé lasán chuig an bpoll;
Is a Dhia! nárbh uafásach an t-ár i measc na nGall —
Píosaí de photaí réabtha ina gceathanna le gaoth.
"Tá tasc ansúd don tincéir," ars' an Gunnadóir Mac Aoidh.

Ach nár thrua linn an t-amharc nuair a ghlan an smúit ina dhiaidh!
Bhí an triúr fear gan anam — Taimí, Paidí agus Liam!
Ghluais na mílte Sasanach dár n-ionsaí ar gach taobh
"Tá deireadh leis an gcluiche," ars' an Gunnadóir Mac Aoidh.

I mBaile na Muc, Dé Sathairn, chailleamar an lá;
Ach ar éacht an Ghunnadóra beidh trácht go lá an bhráth.'
Ar chrann boltraí a crochadh é 's an ghrian ag dul 'na luí:
"A Chríost, bí liom den dul seo," ars' an Gunnadóir Mac Aoidh.

Eoghan Ó Tuairisc

Wolfe Tone

(Air: The Croppy Boy)

The first storm of winter blew high, blew high,
Red leaves were scattering to a gloomy sky;
Rain clouds were lowering o'er the plains of Kildare,
When from Dublin, southward, the mourners came there.

"In the spring," they whispered, "Lord Edward bled,
And the blood of hosts was in summer shed;
Death in the autumn o'er Connacht passed,
But the loss that is sorest came last, came last.

"Though Fitzgerald died, sure we fought them still,
And we shouted 'Vengeance' on Vinegar Hill,
Knowing our flag would again be flown
If France gave ear to the prayers of Tone.

"Twice," we thought, "his appealing lips
Brought forth her armies and battleships,
And the storms of God shall not always stay
England's doom, as in Bantry Bay.

"And oh," we said to the hopeless ones,
Who made count of Ireland's martyred sons,
"The bravest lives; be your mourning dumb,
Ere the snow of winter Wolfe Tone shall come."

He came — was beaten — we bear him here
From a prison cell on his funeral bier,
And Freedom's hope shall be buried low
With his mouldering corpse 'neath the winter snow.

'Hush," one said, o'er the new-set sod,
"Hope shall endure with our faith in God,
And God shall only forsake us when
This grave is forgotten by Irishmen."

Alice Milligan

Alice Milligan (1865-1953) was born in Omagh, Co. Tyrone. She invited John O'Leary, the Fenian, to the '98 Centenary celebrations which she organised in Belfast. She was an organiser for Conradh na Gaeilge and was later honoured with a D.Litt. by the NUI in 1941.

Boolavogue

(Air: Eochaill)

Fr. John Murphy of Boolavogue led his parishioners in routing the Camolin Cavalry on 26th May, 1798. The Wexford insurgents were eventually defeated at Vinegar Hill on 21st June.

At Boolavogue, as the sun was setting
 O'er the bright May meadows of Shelmalier,
A rebel hand set the heather blazing
 And brought the neighbours from far and near.
Then Father Murphy, from old Kilcormack,
 Spurred up the rocks with a warning cry;
"Arm! Arm!" he cried, "for I've come to lead you,
 For Ireland's freedom we fight or die."

He led us on 'gainst the coming soldiers,
 And the cowardly Yeomen we put to flight;
'Twas at the Harrow the boys of Wexford
 Showed Bookey's regiment how men could fight.
Look out for hirelings, King George of England,
 Search every kingdom where breathes a slave,
For Father Murphy of the County Wexford
 Sweeps o'er the land like a mighty wave.

We took Camolin and Enniscorthy,
 And Wexford storming drove out our foes;
'Twas at Sliabh Coillte our pikes were reeking
 With the crimson stream of the beaten Yeos.
At Tubberneering and Ballyellis
 Full many a Hessian lay in his gore;
Ah, Father Murphy, had aid come over
 The green flag floated from shore to shore!

At Vinegar Hill, o'er the pleasant Slaney,
 Our heroes vainly stood back to back,
And the Yeos at Tullow took Father Murphy
 And burned his body upon the rack.
God grant you glory, brave Father Murphy,
 And open heaven to all your men;
The cause that called you may call to-morrow
 In another fight for the Green again.

P. J. McCall (1861-1919)

Na Francaigh Bhána

Tá cuntas anseo ar chuid de eachtraí an Éirí Amach. Is cosúil gur
scríobhadh na véarsaí seo nuair a bhí an pobal díomuach
tar éis ghéilleadh Bhéal Átha na Muc.

Ar an gceathrú lá fichead de mhí na Lúnasa
Bhí na Francaigh againn le bánú an lae;
Is an tír ag bogadh le tréan a bpúdair —
Tuilleadh sciúirse 'teacht ar Chlann na nGael.

Thug muid briseadh ag Crois Mhaoilíona,
Is ag Bealach Gaoithe cuireadh orthu an rotréat,
Ag Caisleán a' Bharra, eadar sin is meán oíche
Bhí dhá chéad 's trí mhíle le síneadh i gcré.

Is luath ar maidin a fuair muid scéala,
Le scaoileadh na bhfáinní is ag bánú an lae —
Scéala nár bhinn linn, is nár mhaith linn trácht air —
Na Francaigh bhána gur gabhadh iad.

An méid a d'imigh acu is nár bádh
Chaith siad an lá sin faoi éadan bruaigh,
Mar shlua caorach ag dul thar sáile,
Agus eagla a mbáite orthu ag gach taobh.

Ar éirí amach dúinn, lá ar na mhárach,
Le scaoileadh na bhfáinní is le bánú an lae,
Bhí trúpa Sasanach i lár na sráide,
Is nach tréan na lámha nach nglacfadh siad.

Bhí a gcuid waggons leo ag ionsaí an tsléibhe,
Agus na bráithre go léir ag guí Dé
Len ár náimhde a leagan, is an bhua a bhaint díofa,
Agus fós an lá a thabhairt do Chlann na nGael.

Mná óga na tíre tá anois gan phósadh,
Tá eagla mhór orm go mbeidh na fir gann,
'Á gcur go Sasan' leis na Francaigh —
In aghaidh rí Sheoirse, níl gar dóibh ann.

Ach tá dúil mhór agam as Rí na nGrásta,
Is as Bonaparte nach ndearna ariamh feall,
Go dtiocfaidh ár gcaraid i measc na námhad,
Is go mbainfidh siad sásamh as Clann na nGall.

Ón mBéaloideas

General Munroe

General Henry Munroe led the Co. Down insurgents, who were victorious at Saintfield, but were defeated at Ballinahinch on 13th June, 1798. He was betrayed and hanged in front of his own home in Lisburn, Co. Antrim on 16th June.

My name is George Campbell at the age of eighteen
I joined the United Men to strive for the green,
And many a battle I did undergo
With that hero commander, brave General Munroe.

Have you heard of the Battle of Ballinahinch
Where the people oppressed rose up in defence?
When Munroe left the mountains his men took the field,
And they fought for twelve hours and never did yield.

Munroe being tired and in want of a sleep,
Gave a woman ten guineas his secret to keep.
But when she got the money the devil tempted her so
That she sent for the soldiers and surrendered Munroe.

The army they came and surrounded the place,
And they took him to Lisburn and lodged him in jail.
And his father and mother in passing that way
Heard the very last words that their dear son did say!

"Oh, I die for my country as I fought for her cause,
And I don't fear your soldiers nor yet heed your laws.
And let every true man who hates Ireland's foe
Fight bravely for freedom like Henry Munroe."

And 'twas early one morning when the sun was still low,
They murdered our hero brave General Munroe,
And high o'er the Courthouse stuck his head on a spear,
For to make the United men tremble and fear.

Then up came Munroe's sister, she was all dressed in green,
With a sword by her side that was well-sharped and keen.
Giving three hearty cheers, away she did go
Saying, "I'll have revenge for my brother Munroe."

All ye good men who listen, just think of the fate
Of the brave men who died in the year Ninety Eight.
For poor old Ireland would be free long ago
If her sons were all rebels like Henry Munroe.

Dublin Castle, 30th *August*, 1798.

ADVICES have been received this Morning from the Head Quarters of the Lord Lieutenant, at *Athlone*, by which it appears that his Excellency, having collected a very confiderable Force, intended to move forward this Morning, with a View to bring the Enemy to Action as foon as poffible.

There are yet no Accounts of the Enemy having advanced beyond *Caftlebar*.

Lieutenant General *Lake* was at *Tuam*, and is to form a Junction with the Lord Lieutenant. Brigadier General *Taylor* is at *Boyle*.

DUBLIN: Printed by GEORGE GRIERSON, Printer to the KING's Moft Excellent Majefty.

Bonny Bunch of Roses

(The bunch of roses is said to represent England, Scotland and Ireland. The Air is a variant of "An Beinsín Luachra".

By the margin of the ocean, one pleasant evening in the month of June,
When all those feathered songsters their liquid notes did sweetly tune,
'Twas there I spied a female, and on her features the signs of woe,
Conversing with young Bonaparte, concerning the Bonny Bunch of Roses, O.

Then up speaks young Napoleon, and takes his mother by the hand,
Saying: "Mother dear, be patient until I'm able to take command;
And I'll raise a mighty army, and through tremendous dangers go,
And I never will return again till I've conquered the Bonny Bunch of Roses, O.

"When first you saw great Bonaparte, you fell upon your bended knee,
And you asked your father's life of him, he granted it right manfully,
And 'twas then he took his army, and o'er the frozen Alps did go,
And he said: 'I'll conquer Moscow, and return for the Bonny Bunch of Roses, O.'

"He took three hundred thousand men, and kings likewise to bear his throne,
He was so well provided for, that he could sweep the world alone;
But when he came to Moscow, he was overpowered by the sleet and snow,
With Moscow all a-blazing, and he lost the Bonny Bunch of Roses, O."

"Now son, be not too venturesome, for in England are the hearts of oak,
And England, Ireland, Scotland, their unity shall ne'er be broke;
Remember your brave father, in Saint Helena he lies low,
And if you follow after, beware of the Bonny Bunch of Roses, O."

"O mother, adieu for ever, for now I lie on my dying bed,
If I lived I'd have been clever, but now I droop my youthful head;
But when our bones lie mouldering and weeping willows o'er us grow,
The deeds of young Napoleon shall blanch the Bonny Bunch of Roses, O."

ARMY OF IRELAND.

LIBERTY   EQUALITY.

Head quarters at Castlebar, 14th Fructidor, sixth Year of the French Republic, One and Indivisible.

"General Humbert, Commander in Chief of the Army of Ireland, desirous of organizing with the least possible delay, an administrative power for the Province of Connaught, decrees as follows :

" 1.   The Government of the Province of Connaught shall reside at Castlebar till further orders.

" 2.   The Government shall be composed of twelve members, who shall be named by the General in chief of the French Army.

" 3.   Citizen JOHN MOORE is named President of the Government of the Province of Connaught, he is specially entrusted with the nomination and reunion of the members of the Government.

" 4.   The Government shall occupy itself immediately in organizing the Military power of the Province of Connaught, and with providing subsistence for the French and Irish Armies.

" 5.   There shall be organized eight regiments of infantry, each of twelve hundred men, and four regiments of Cavalry, each of six hundred men.

" 6.   The Government shall declare rebels and traitors to the country all those who having received clothing and arms, shall not join the army within four and twenty hours.

" 7.   Every individual from sixteen years of age to forty, inclusive, is REQUIRED in the name of the Irish Republic, to betake himself instantly to the French Camp, to march in a mass against the common enemy, the Tyrant of ANGLICIZED IRELAND, whose destruction alone can establish the independence and happiness of ANCIENT HIBERNIA.

" The General Commanding-in-Chief
HUMBERT.

55

Maidin Luain Chincíse

Amhrán maorga uasal ar an Éirí Amach i Loch Garman

Maidin Luain Chincíse labhair an síofra sa ngleann,
Do bhailíodar na cága chun ábhacht a dhéanamh ann;
Do chruinníomar 'na dtimpeall is do lasamar ár dtinte,
Agus thógamar ceo draíochta go haoibhinn os a gceann.

Is mó baile margaidh agus cathair aoibhinn cheoil
Agus cúirt ages na Sasanaigh chun seasamh ann 'nár gcomhair;
Beir scéala cruinn abhaile uainn Dé Domhnaigh go dtí an Aifreann
Gur chun sléibhe a cuireadh chun reatha sinn 'nár seasamh insa ngleo.

Dá bhfeicfeása an buachaill is an cailín ceannbhuí cas,
Do bhíodh ag imeacht suas ar thuairisc na bhfear;
Beir scéala cruinn dóibh uaimse go bhfuil Captaen Lambert fuar lag
Ar thaobh an tsléibhe go huaigneach gan tuama air ná leac.

Cá bhfuilid na Muimhnigh nó an fíor go mairid beo,
Ná cruinníd siad 'nár dtimpeall is cabhrú linn sa ngleo?
Mar is deacair poirt do stríocadh ná clanna búir do dhíbirt
Ón ár mbailte dúchais dílis bhí ag ár sinsir riamh romhainn.

Do tháinig aniar ó Chonnacht chughainn céad is míle laoch,
An oiread céanna ó Ulaidh chughainn i bhfoirm cheart 's i bhfaobhar,
Suaimhneas lae níor tugadh dóibh gur bhuaileamar bualadh is fiche orthu,
'Sé mo léan mar sileadh fuil is coirp ár bhfear i ndeireadh lae.

Beir scéala suas chun Mumhan uainn, a rún ghil 's a stór,
Agus inis an scéal faoi chumha dóibh go bhfuil an sciúirse 'nár gcomhair;
Mar is mó leanbh fireann fionn geal agus ainnir mhilis mhúinte
Agus ógfhear cliste lúfar san úir uainn ag feo.

Mo léan ar an Mhumhain nár éirigh nuair d'adhnamar an gleo;
Faoi airm ghreanta ghreadhnmhar i bhfaghairt acu 'nár gcomhair,
D'fhágadar go tréith sinn is neart ár namhad 'nár dtimpeall,
Ach grá mo chroí na Laighnigh b'iad d'adhain an tine leo.

Mícheál Óg Ó Longáin

Mícheál Óg Ó Longáin

Ceaptar gur rugadh Mícheál Óg Ó Longáin i nGleann Corbhraí in Iarthar Luimnigh i 1766. Ba i gCarraig na bhFear, Co. Chorcaí, áfach, a d'fhás sé suas. Scoláire Gaeilge a bhí ann agus chuaigh sé isteach ins na hÉireannaigh Aontaithe i 1797.

Deirtear gur scríobh sé an sár-amhrán "Sliabh na mBan" ach níl sé cinnte. Ba i gCarraig Mhoicléir, lámh le Sliabh na mBan a tharla an troid ar 25ú Iúil 1798. Briseadh ar na Gaeil. Tá stíl an amhráin ar aon dul le "Maidin Luain Chincíse" agus táimid cinnte gur tháinig sé sin ó pheann Uí Longáin.

Scríobh sé freisin "Do Chuala Scéal do Réab mo Chroí Ionam" ar chloisteáil dó gur gabhadh an Tiarna Éamonn Mac Gearailt, an tArd-Cheannasaí Míleata ar na hÉireannaigh Aontaithe.

Fuair sé saol fada, rinne sé a lán oibre ar lámhscríbhinní Gaeilge agus bhailigh sé stór mór seanfhocal. Fuair sé bás i 1840.

C.MacC.

The Heroine of Ross

An incident of the insurrection of 1798. The heroine was a girl named Molly Doyle, of Castleboro. She persuaded her father to return home because of his age and she took his place in the Insurgent ranks.

Up from fitful sleep we wakened at the first kiss of the day;
There was silence by our watchfires, for we knew the task that lay
To be wrought to joy or ruin ere the stars should look again
On the places of our childhood — hill and river, rath and glen.

We were thinking of the dear ones that we left to face the foe,
And we prayed for all the brave ones that were lying cold and low,
And we looked upon the meadows staring blank against the sun,
Then we thought upon the future and the work that must be done.

Fear! we knew not, for Vengeance burned fierce in every heart;
Doubt! why doubt, when we but hungered each to do a true man's part?
"On to Ross!" our pulses quickened as the word from man to man
Passed along, and brave John Kelly forward stepped to lead the van.

Through the misty summer morn by the hedgerows bright we sped,
While the lark with joyous music filled the spreading dome o'erhead.
And the sun rode up the circle, and the earth began to smile,
But our hearts knew nought of pleasure, they were cold as ice the while.

Silent all, with stony gaze, and lips as tightly locked as death,
On we went by flowering thorns through the balmy summer's breath,
On, till Ross was close upon us, then a shout resounding rose,
And like ocean's waves in winter in we leaped upon our foes!

For a brief, brief spell they quavered, then their muskets rang reply,
And our boys in hundreds falling looked their last upon the sky.
But, the empty places filling, still we rallied to the fray,
Till the misty summer morning wore into the dusty day.

Then a figure rose above us, 'twas a girl's fragile frame,
And among the fallen soldiers there she walked with eyes aflame,
And her voice rang o'er the clamour like a trumpet o'er the sea:
"Who so dares to die for Ireland, let him come and follow me."

Then against the line of soldiers with a gleaming scythe on high,
Lo! she strode, and though their bullets whistled round, they passed her by,
And a thousand bosoms throbbing, one wild surging shout we gave,
And we swept them from our pathway like the sand before the wave.

William Rooney

Rody MacCorley

Ho! see the fleetfoot hosts of men
Who speed with faces wan,
From farmstead and from fisher's cot
Upon the banks of Bann.
They come with vengeance in their eyes.
Too late, too late are they.
For Rody MacCorley goes to die
On the Bridge of Toome today.

Oh Ireland, Mother Ireland,
You love them still the best;
The fearless brave who fighting fall,
Upon your hapless breast;
But never a one of all your dead
More bravely fell in fray,
Than he who marches to his fate
On the Bridge of Toome today.

Up the narrow street he stepped
Smiling and proud and young;
About the hemp-rope on his neck
The golden ringlets clung.
There's never a tear in the blue, blue eyes
Both glad and bright are they;
As Rody MacCorley goes to die
On the Bridge of Toome today.

Ah! when he last stepped up that street
His shining pike in hand,
Behind him marched in grim array
A stalwart earnest band!
For Antrim town! for Antrim town!
He led them to the fray —
And Rody MacCorley goes to die
On the Bridge of Toome today.

The grey coat and its sash of green
Were brave and stainless then;
A banner flashed beneath the sun
Over the marching men —
The coat hath many a rent this noon
The sash is torn away,
And Rody MacCorley goes to die
On the Bridge of Toome today.

Oh! how his pike flashed to the sun!
Then found a foeman's heart!
Through furious fight, and heavy odds
He bore a true man's part;
And many a red-coat bit the dust
Before his keen pike-play —
But Rody MacCorley goes to die
On the Bridge of Toome today.

Because he loved the Motherland,
Because he loved the Green,
He goes to meet the martyr's fate
With proud and joyous mien,
True to the last, true to the last,
He treads the upward way —
Young Rody MacCorley goes to die
On the Bridge of Toome today.

Ethna Carbery

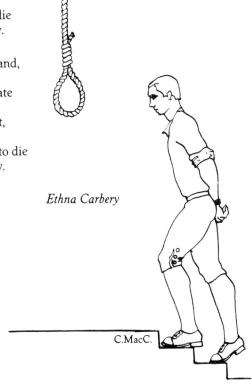

C.MacC.

Ethna Carbery was the penname of Anna MacManus, née Johnston, who was born in Ballymena, Co. Antrim in 1866. She and Alice Milligan founded the paper called The Northern Patriot *and afterwards another called* The Shan Van Vocht. *She was married to the Donegal writer and folklorist, Séamus MacManus, and died in 1902.*

The West's Asleep

When all beside a vigil keep,
The West's asleep, the West's asleep —
Alas! and well may Erin weep
When Connacht lies in slumber deep.
There lake and plain smile fair and free,
'Mid rocks their guardian chivalry.
Sing, Oh! let man learn liberty
From crashing wind and lashing sea.

That chainless wave and lovely land
Freedom and nationhood demand;
Be sure the great God never planned
For slumb'ring slaves a home so grand.
And long a brave and haughty race
Honoured and sentinelled the place.
Sing, Oh! not even their sons' disgrace
Can quite destroy their glory's trace.

For often, in O'Connor's van,
To triumph dashed each Connacht clan,
And fleet as deer the Normans ran
Thro' Corrsliabh Pass and Ardrahan;
And later times saw deeds as brave,
And glory guards Clanricarde's grave,
Sing, Oh! they died their land to save
At Aughrim's slopes and Shannon's wave.

And if, when all a vigil keep,
The West's asleep! the West's asleep!
Alas! and well may Erin weep
That Connacht lies in slumber deep.
But, hark! a voice like thunder spake,
The West's awake! the West's awake!
Sing, Oh! hurrah! let England quake,
We'll watch till death for Erin's sake!

Thomas Davis

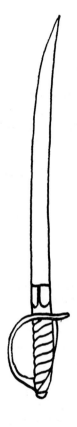

Donncha an Rópa

The Right Hon. Denis Browne was High Sheriff of Co. Mayo in 1798. He was a brother of Lord Altamont and dealt savagely with those who had participated in the Rising or helped in any way. It was said that for months afterwards, he had a man hanged in Castlebar every day. Sometimes he presided personally at the executions.

Richard Jordan of Rooskey, who with Séamas Bán Ó Máille, led the capture of Claremorris, was informed on, but Denis Browne in a letter to Lord Hardwick said "it would be difficult to find an unprejudiced jury to try him". A courtmartial was arranged and Jordan sentenced to death. Browne arranged the execution for Claremorris, where the prisoner "committed the acts of treason of which he was convicted". He then added, in his letter to the Lord Lieutenant:

> "I shall not fail to attend there and will further your Excellency's intention of making the example as impressive as possible."

The Secret Service List shows that the informer who betrayed Richard Jordan was paid one hundred guineas.

It was estimated that Denis Browne had 200 men hanged, 200 transported and 100 more pressed into service in the British Army overseas or salt mines on the Continent.

Dúghlas de hÍde collected the song "Na Buachaillí Bána" in Co. Mayo in 1903 and published it as a song ascribed to Antaine Ó Reachtabhra. The song had never before been written down because it would have been too dangerous. (There is a record in a manuscript in the British Museum of a man being arrested in Oranmore for drinking the toast, *'That the King's skin may be converted into boats for Bonaparte,* which wish was inserted in a song that was sung in ale-houses and whiskey-shops.")

Dúghlas de hÍde records that the tree used as a gallows in Castlebar was still standing in 1903, but by the time Richard Hayes was researching his "Last Invasion of Ireland" in the 1930s it had been uprooted by a storm.

Denis Browne was called "Donncha an Rópa" by the people of Co. Mayo and their feelings about him were well expressed in the first stanza of "Na Buachaillí Bána", excellently translated by de hÍde, who described it as "giota fíochmhar".

Na Buachaillí Bána

A Dhonncha Brúin 's deas do chraithfinn lámh leat
Agus ní le grá duit ach le fonn do ghabháil (góail)
Cheanglóinn suas thú le rópa cnáibe
Agus chuirfinn mo "Spír" i do bholg mór.
Mar is iomaí buachaill maith chuir tú thar sáile
Thiocfas anall fós is cúnamh leo
Faoi chultaibh dearga agus hataí lása
'S beidh an droma Francach a' seinm leo!

The Whiteboys

If I got your hand, it is I would take it
But not to shake it, O Denis Browne,
But to hang you high with a hempen cable
And your feet unable to find the ground.
For it's many's the boy who was strong and able
You sent in chains with your tyrant frown;
But they'll come again, with the French flag waving
And the French drums raving to strike you down!

Tone Is Coming Back Again

This song to a traditional air, has been popular in Ulster since the days of the United Irishmen.

Cheer up, brave hearts, to-morrow's dawn will see us march again
Beneath old Erin's flag of green that ne'er has known a stain.
And ere our hands the sword shall yield or furled that banner be —
We swear to make our native land from the tyrant's thraldom free!

Chorus
For Tone is coming back again with legions o'er the wave,
The scions of Lord Clare's Brigade, the dear old land to save,
For Tone is coming back again with legions o'er the wave
The dear old land, the loved old land, the brave old land to save!

Though crouching minions preach to us to be the Saxon's slave,
We'll teach them all what pikes can do when hearts are true and brave.
Fling Freedom's banner to the breeze, let it float o'er land and sea —
We swear to make our native land from the tyrant's thraldom free!

Chorus

Young Dwyer 'mong the heath-clad hills of Wicklow leads his men;
And Russell's voice stirs kindred hearts in many an Ulster glen;
Brave Father Murphy's men march on from the Barrow to the sea —
We swear to make our native land from the tyrant's thraldom free!

Chorus

Too long we've borne with smouldering wrath the cursed alien laws,
That wreck our shrines and burn our homes and crush our country's cause;
But now the day has come at last; Revenge our watchword be!
We swear to make our native land from the tyrant's thraldom free!

Chorus

Tom Gilheaney

It happened once upon a time
As sages tell in phrase sublime;
That Tom Gilheaney stout and straight
Prepared his pike in ninety-eight,
And from Drumkeeran did advance
To join the gallant sons of France.

Thus hastily equipped for war
He journeyed on to Castlebar,
Where there he showed good Irish play
Before the Saxons ran away.
It made him joyful to behold
The flutter of the green and gold
And oftentimes that day he said,
"Thank God the green waves o'er the red".

Next morning for Collooney then
He marched with the Killala men,
Where victory again did smile
Upon the banners of our Isle.
The rank and file, with lances long,
Unfailing nerves and sinews strong,
The vengeful mandate did obey,
Which made them victors of the day.

To see how foemen reeled and ran
Was balsam for an Irishman.
Besides the band conjointly played
In thundering strains, "The White Cockade",
And brilliant was Gilheaney's luck,
'Til he arrived at Ballinamuck.

(There are 27 more stanzas to this song)

C.MacC.

Ó 'bhean a' tí

Ó éirigí suas a thogha na bhfear,
Is cuirigí píce 'r bharr gach cleith.
Is leagaigí síos iad lucht an droch-chroí
Agus cuirigí dlí na Frainc' ar bun.
Agus ó bhean a' tí, cén bhuairt sin ort?

Is ó bhean a' tí fá dhó nó trí
Beidh talamh gan chíos ón bhliain seo amach againn,
Is ó bhean a' tí, nach suairc é sin?

Tá jug ar an mbord is tá beoir ag teacht,
Tá arm go leor ag an Duke of York.
Tá 'n Francach 's an Spáinneach ar bhruach na trá,
Agus b'fhearr liom go mór é ná comhrá ban,
Agus ó bhean a' tí, cén bhuairt sin ort?

Chualas aréir na daoine á rá
Go raibh Cathair Chorcaí á dó go lár;
Go raibh Ginearál Hoche is a chlaíomh chinn óir
Ag réiteach an róid do Bhonaparte;
Agus ó bhean a' tí, cén bhuairt sin ort?

Ó shuigh mise síos 's mo mhian le m'ais,
Ag ól mo cháirt dí mar dhéanfadh fear;
Sé dúirt bean a' tí den chomhrá mhín,
Gan airgead síos bí 'gabháil amach,
Agus ó bhean a' ti, cén bhuairt sin ort?

Seo é leagan Béarla ar an gcéad véarsa:

Come! rise in your might, O best of men,
And muster your pikes in yonder glen;
Your enemies smite, with sword and lance,
And no laws you will own, but those of France.
    And O! bhean a' tí, what ails thee now?
        O! bhean a' tí, in two years or three
            You'll have land without rent to graze your cow on,
    And O! bhean a' tí, what ails thee now?

Plant, Plant the Tree

During the years of the Revolution, the French planted Trees of Liberty in their towns and villages. The custom spread throughout Europe and reached Ireland as early as 1792.

Chorus

     Plant, plant the tree, fair Freedom's tree
     Midst danger, wounds and slaughter
     Erin's green fields its soil shall be,
     Her tyrant's blood its water.

They come, they come, see myriads come
Of Frenchmen to relieve us;
Seize, seize the pike, beat, beat the drum,
They come, my friends, to save us;
Whilst trembling despots fly this land,
To shun impending danger,
We'll stretch forth our fraternal hand,
To hail each welcome stranger.

Those nicknames, Marquis, Lord and Earl,
That set the crowd a-gazing,
We prize as hogs esteem a pearl,
Their patents set a-blazing,
No more they'll vote away our wealth
To please a king or queen, sirs,
But gladly pack away by stealth,
Or taste the Guillotine, sirs.

C.MacC.

The Parliament, who say foresooth
They represent the nation,
Shall scamper East, West, North and South,
Or feel our indignation.
The Speaker's mace to current coin
We presently will alter,
For ribbons lately thought so fine,
We'll fit each with a halter.

And when th'all glorious work is done,
Rejoice with one another,
To ploughshares beat the sword and gun,
Now every man's your brother;
Detested wars shall ever cease
In kind fraternisation,
All will be harmony and peace,
And the whole world one nation.

Dublin Castle, 8th September, 1798.

ADVICES have been received this Evening from Head
Quarters at *Carrick on Shannon,* by which it appears that
the Enemy had passed through *Manor Hamilton,* and cros-
sed the *Shannon* at *Ballintra.* They threw away eight
Guns and two Tumbrils in their March, and many of the
Inhabitants who had joined, were deserting them. General *Lake* was following them with his Corps. His Excellency was marching upon *Mohill.*

A Body of Insurgents having collected near *Granard,*
on *Wednesday* last, several Yeoman Corps in the Neigh-
bourhood, and from the County of *Cavan,* commanded by
Captain *Cottingham,* collected with Celerity, and entirely
defeated the Insurgents at the Town of *Granard,* killing
about One Hundred and Fifty, and dispersing the Re-
mainder. The Yeomanry experienced no Loss.

On the same Evening Lord *Longford,* at the Head of a
Body of Yeomanry, assisted by a Detachment of the King's
Troops, attacked a Body of Rebels at *Wilson's Hospital,*
and put them to Flight, with much Slaughter.

DUBLIN: Printed by GEORGE GRIERSON, Printer to the KING's Most Excellent Majesty.

The Boys of Wexford

In comes the captain's daughter, the captain of the Yeos,
Saying "Brave United Irishman, we'll ne'er again be foes.
A thousand pounds I'll give you and fly from home with thee,
And dress myself in man's attire and fight for liberty."

Chorus
We are the boys of Wexford, who fought with heart and hand
To burst in twain the galling chain and free our native land.

"I want no gold, my maiden fair, to fly from home with thee;
Your shining eyes will be my prize — more dear than gold to me.
I want no gold to nerve my arm to do a true man's part —
To free my land I'd gladly give the red drops from my heart."

Chorus

And when we left our cabins, boys, we left with right good will
To see our friends and neighbours that were at Vinegar Hill!
A young man from our Irish ranks a cannon he let go;
He slapt it into Lord Mountjoy — a tyrant he laid low!

Chorus

We bravely fought and conquered at Ross and Wexford town;
Three Bullet Gate for years to come will speak for our renown;
Through Walpole's horse and Walpole's foot on Tubberneering's day,
Depending on the long, bright pike, and well it worked its way.

Chorus

And Oulart's name shall be their shame, whose steel we ne'er did fear,
For every man could do his part like Forth and Shelmalier!
And if, for want of leaders, we lost at Vinegar Hill,
We're ready for another fight, and love our country still!

Chorus

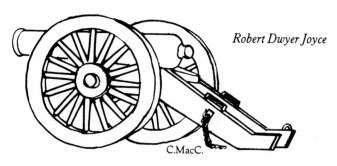

Robert Dwyer Joyce

C.MacC.

70

Do Chuala Scéal

Do chuala scéal do réab mo chroí ionam
Is d'ardaigh guais is gruaim ar m'intinn,
Scéal do léan fir Éireann timpeall
Is ler cuireadh Fódhla i mbrón gan scaoileadh.

A Chlanna Gael, sin réidh sibh choíche;
D'imigh bhur dtreoir, níl speois ná brí ionaibh
Sin é an Gearaltach ceangailte i ngeimhleach
Is Artúr uasal uaibh thar taoide.*

Níl rí-fhlaith stáit le fáil san tír seo
Lenar mhaith bhur nglas a scaoileadh,
Ná fuil mí-ádh agus díobháil nimhe air
Is an chinniúint dá chiorrú is dá chloíchaint.

Ní hionadh liomsa búir go haoibhinn
Gan baol, gan bascadh, gan mairg i gCríoch Loirc,
Is gur sibh féin atá, cé náir le hinsint,
Ag braith a chéile do thréad na gclaoin-bheart.

Iarraim, aitim is screadaim ar Íosa,
Is go raibh an geall ar namhaid ár dtíre;
Go raibh baol is léan is líonrith,
Ar gach spreasán creacháin coimhthíoch.

Rí na bhflaitheas do dhealbhaigh tíortha;
Ré agus réalta, spéartha is taoide,
Go ndéana cúl go humhal dár muintir,
Is go raibh an cluiche seo acu gan righneas.

Ó chím an cás mar atá ag ár muintir,
Is go bhfuil na búir go dlúth 'na dtimpeall,
Preabfad chun siúil anonn thar taoide
Is tiocfad anall le Francaigh líofa.

Go bhfeiceam Éire saor gan daoirse,
Is an bhratainn uaithne in uachtar scaoilte,
Gach tíoránach claoin-cheardach, coimhthíoch,
In ainm an diabhail, is gan Dia dá gcoimhdeacht.

Mícheál Óg Ó Longáin

* *An Tiarna Éamonn Mac Gearailt agus Artúr Ó Conchúir.*

"After having obtained the greatest successes and made the arms of the French Republic triumph during my stay in Ireland, I have at length been obliged to submit to a superior force of 30,000 troops." — General Humbert's Report to the French Directory after Ballinamuck.

71

The Wearing of the Green

(Old Version, 1798)

I met with Napper Tandy,
　　And he took me by the hand.
Saying: How is poor old Ireland,
　　And what way does she stand?
She's the most distressful country,
　　That ever yet was seen.
They are hanging men and women,
　　For the wearing of the green.

Chorus:

　　For the wearing of the green,
　　For the wearing of the green.
　　My native land, I cannot stand,
　　For the wearing of the green.

My father loved you tenderly,
　　He lies within your breast.
While I, that would have died for you,
　　Must never so be blessed.
For laws, their cruel laws, have said,
　　That seas should roll between
Old Ireland and her faithful sons,
　　Who love to wear the green.

Chorus:

I care not for the Thistle,
　　And I care not for the Rose;
When bleak winds round us whistle,
　　Neither down nor crimson shows.
But like hope to him that's friendless,
　　When no joy around is seen.
O'er our graves with love that's endless,
　　Blooms our own immortal green.

Chorus:

The Green Linnet

*"Maria Louisa's Lamentation for the Loss of her Lover". The Green Linnet was
Napoleon Bonaparte. The air is a variant of "Uilleagán Dubh Ó".*

Curiosity led a young native of Erin
    To view the gay banks of the Rhine,
Where an empress he saw, and the robe she was wearing
    All over with diamonds did shine.
No goddess in splendour was ever yet seen
    To equal this fair maid so mild and serene,
In soft murmurs she cried, "O my Linnet so green,
    Sweet Boney, will I ne'er see you more?

The cold lofty Alps you freely passed over,
    Which nature had placed in your way:
At Marengo, Bellona around you did hover,
    And Paris rejoiced the next day.
It grieved me the hardships that you did undergo,
    The mountains you traversed all covered with snow,
And the balance of power your courage laid low:
    Sweet Boney, will I ne'er see you more?

The crowned heads of Europe when you were in splendour,
    Swore that they would have you subdue;
But the goddess of freedom soon made them surrender,
    And lower their standard to you.
Old Frederick's colours to France he did bring;
    Yet offspring found shelter under your wing;
That year at Vienna you sweetly did sing;
    Sweet Boney, will I ne'er see you more?

What numbers of men there were eager to slay you!
    Their malice you viewed with a smile;
Their gold through all Europe was found to betray you;
    They joined with the Mamelukes at the Nile
Like ravenous vultures their vile passions did burn;
    The orphans they slew and caused widows to mourn;
But my Linnet is gone, and he ne'er will return:
    Sweet Boney, will I ne'er see you more?

I ranged through the deserts of wild Abyssinia,
    And could yet find no cure for my pain;
I will go and inquire at the isle of St. Helena,
    But soft murmurs whisper 'Tis vain'!
Come, tell me, ye critics come tell me in time,
    What nations I'll rove my green Linnet to find;
Was he slain at Waterloo, in Spain or on the Rhine?
    No, he's dead on St. Helena's bleak shore."

Far may the boughs of Liberty extend,
    For ever cultured by the brave and free;
For ever blasted be the impious hand
    That lops one branch from this noble tree!
Patriots, 'tis yours to make her verdure thrive,
    And keep the roots of Liberty alive.

This "treasonable document" was found on a Co. Westmeath Republican called John Reilly, in September, 1798, following the Battle of Wilson's Hospital. He was flogged but managed to escape and hid in a clump of rushes until the redcoats gave up the search.